OPENING DOORS TO YOUR
LIMITLESS POTENTIAL

DAILY MOTIVATIONS
AND AFFIRMATIONS

Mitch Mitchell, Ph.D.

Dedication

This book is dedicated to the countless number of people on the precipice of their breakthrough, awakening, and achievement. This book is dedicated to those devoted to seeking the best version of themselves.

Forward

This book was written at a critical time in our lives. We are facing a high paced society that often perpetuates anxiety, self-doubt, anger, obsession and depression. If we are not mindful of the ways we perceive and address pressures from home, work, and in our community, we will become the victim in our own "would be" success story. These daily activities challenge us to think critically about successes, failures, and opportunities to grow. As I did the daily reflective writing activities, it helped me become more reflective of what or whom I was thankful for and mindful of how my perception influenced how well I was solving the challenges I faced. Each quote seemed to come right on time for me. I am thankful for how this book has empowered me to grow. Many thanks to Dr. Mitchell for this amazing book.

Kenneth Vaughan, Ed.D.

Assistant Principal for Atlanta Public Schools

Introduction

Open the cover to an inspirational guide of quotes, thoughts, encouragements, and practices connecting you to your goals to lead you to your achievements. This tool is intended to help you channel your energy and ignite your passion to achieve the unthinkable... and to be the best version of yourself. These daily quotes and affirmations are powerful motivations for a range of life topics from advice, dream achieving, leadership, success, goal setting, and more. There's no manual to success; however, routines, behaviors, and practices transfer to performance which leads to breakthroughs and successes. I challenge you to commit to yourself for the next 90 days.

Note from the Author

Since 2009, these quotes have been created and curated as a result of my thoughts and life experiences. They've guided me through adversity and served as a reminder to remain true to myself, my goals, and my dreams. It was important for me to chronicle these moments derived from life-lessons, personal challenges, and triumphs for others to use as motivation to achieve anything they put their mind and energy towards.

Develop.
Grow.
Motivate.

Sometimes great outcomes have rocky starts.

Today I am thankful for ...

_____

_____

_____

_____

_____

_____

_____

What rocky starts did you surmount today?

_____

_____

_____

_____

_____

_____

_____

It's already yours. There are blessings with your name on it. When are you going to get what's already yours?

Today I am thankful for ...

_____

_____

_____

_____

_____

_____

_____

What did you do to get what's already yours today?

_____

_____

_____

_____

_____

_____

Don't major in the minor.
Focus on what's important.

Today I am thankful for ...

_____

_____

_____

_____

_____

_____

_____

What did you major in today?

_____

_____

_____

_____

_____

_____

_____

To expand, continue creating new experiences, new opportunities, and networks. Everything changes as we grow.

Today I am thankful for ...

_____

_____

_____

_____

_____

_____

_____

What did you create today?

_____

_____

_____

_____

_____

_____

_____

As we grow so does the world around us.

Today I am thankful for ...

_____

_____

_____

_____

_____

_____

_____

How did you grow today?

_____

_____

_____

_____

_____

_____

_____

Everything that is great must be measured.

Today I am thankful for ...

_____

_____

_____

_____

_____

_____

How did you work your greatness today? How did you measure it?

_____

_____

_____

_____

_____

_____

_____

You don't discover the "real ones", until you go through something real.

Today I am thankful for ...

_____

_____

_____

_____

_____

_____

_____

What "real ones" did you discover?

_____

_____

_____

_____

_____

_____

_____

_____

We are all transitioning through a halfway house, halfway from where we came from and halfway to where we are going.

Today I am thankful for ...

_____

_____

_____

_____

_____

_____

_____

What transitions did you go through today?

_____

_____

_____

_____

_____

_____

_____

Progress is progress, no matter how minuscule the movement.

Today I am thankful for ...

_____

_____

_____

_____

_____

_____

_____

What progress did you make today?

_____

_____

_____

_____

_____

_____

_____

Never ask anyone to believe in you if you don't believe in yourself.

Today I am thankful for ...

_____
_____
_____
_____
_____
_____
_____

How did you believe in yourself today?

_____
_____
_____
_____
_____
_____
_____

The first step to an answer is a question. Never be afraid to ask.

Today I am thankful for ...

_____

_____

_____

_____

_____

_____

_____

What questions did you ask today?

_____

_____

_____

_____

_____

_____

Big flowers outgrow small pots.

Today I am thankful for ...

_____

_____

_____

_____

_____

_____

How did you grow today?

_____

_____

_____

_____

_____

_____

_____

Motivation without determination results in stagnation.

Today I am thankful for ...

_____

_____

_____

_____

_____

_____

_____

What were you determined to do today?

_____

_____

_____

_____

_____

_____

Progressive thinking is keeping your head up and your eyes directed onward. Let your eyes guide you forward.

Today I am thankful for ...

_____

_____

_____

_____

_____

_____

How did you progress today?

_____

_____

_____

_____

_____

_____

_____

Everybody has secret talents within them; it's up to you to discover your hidden treasure.

Today I am thankful for ...

_____

_____

_____

_____

_____

_____

_____

How did you show your talent today?

_____

_____

_____

_____

_____

_____

_____

It only takes a right turn to get on the right track.

Today I am thankful for ...

_____

_____

_____

_____

_____

_____

_____

What right turns did you make today?

_____

_____

_____

_____

_____

_____

_____

> # There is strength in numbers; however, the testament of an individual is when they stand when no one else is around.

Today I am thankful for ...

_____

_____

_____

_____

_____

_____

What test did you pass today?

_____

_____

_____

_____

_____

_____

Motivation leads us.
Direction guides us.
Determination drives us.

Today I am thankful for ...

_____

_____

_____

_____

_____

_____

What motivated you today?

_____

_____

_____

_____

_____

_____

_____

You won't learn how much you can lift until you take a risk and test your strength.

Today I am thankful for ...

_____

_____

_____

_____

_____

_____

_____

What risk did you take to test your strength today?

_____

_____

_____

_____

_____

_____

_____

Perseverance is the characteristic that separates defeatists from achievers.

Today I am thankful for ...

_____

_____

_____

_____

_____

_____

_____

How did you perservere to achieve today?

_____

_____

_____

_____

_____

_____

_____

The greatest failure in life is to not try.

Today I am thankful for ...

_____

_____

_____

_____

_____

_____

_____

How did you try today?

_____

_____

_____

_____

_____

_____

A flower must be replanted into a larger pot to flourish.

Today I am thankful for ...

_____

_____

_____

_____

_____

_____

_____

How did you flourish today?

_____

_____

_____

_____

_____

_____

_____

Your value increases when you continue believing and investing in yourself?

Today I am thankful for ...

_____

_____

_____

_____

_____

_____

How did you invest in yourself today?

_____

_____

_____

_____

_____

_____

Today we embark upon new challenges and events. Remember yesterday's obstacles prepared you for today's battles.

Today I am thankful for ...

_____

_____

_____

_____

_____

_____

_____

How did yesterday's obstacles prepare you for today?

_____

_____

_____

_____

_____

_____

_____

Occasionally we look down on our situation. Why don't we look out and beyond it?

Today I am thankful for ...

_____
_____
_____
_____
_____
_____
_____

What situation did you look beyond today?

_____
_____
_____
_____
_____
_____
_____

You can't hear your calling because you're too busy on the other line. Stop ignoring your call.

Today I am thankful for ...

_____

_____

_____

_____

_____

_____

_____

How did you answer your calling today?

_____

_____

_____

_____

_____

_____

_____

To be the best means striving and working harder than the rest.

Today I am thankful for ...

_____

_____

_____

_____

_____

_____

How did you strive and work harder today?

_____

_____

_____

_____

_____

_____

One moment does not define who you are or what you have done; a collection of events determines your life as distinguished.

Today I am thankful for ...

_____

_____

_____

_____

_____

_____

_____

How have you worked on being distinguished today?

_____

_____

_____

_____

_____

_____

_____

Adversity either showcases our greatness or exposes our areas of growth.

Today I am thankful for ...

_____
_____
_____
_____
_____
_____
_____

What adversity did you face today?

_____
_____
_____
_____
_____
_____
_____

Our outcome is generated by our input.

Today I am thankful for ...

_____

_____

_____

_____

_____

_____

What outcomes did you generate today?

_____

_____

_____

_____

_____

_____

The good thing about hitting rock bottom is you're no longer digging a hole for yourself. Seize the moment now; it's time to build a solid foundation and push upward.

Today I am thankful for ...

_____

_____

_____

_____

_____

How did you seize the moment today? What foundations are you building?

_____

_____

_____

_____

_____

Your candle will continue to appear dim until you stop comparing it to the sun.

Today I am thankful for ...

_____

_____

_____

_____

_____

_____

_____

How did you shine today?

_____

_____

_____

_____

_____

_____

An intelligent person knows their shortcomings; however, a wise person does not let their faults limit their abilities.

Today I am thankful for ...

_____

_____

_____

_____

_____

_____

_____

What wisdom did you demonstrate today?

_____

_____

_____

_____

_____

_____

_____

It's not about who gets to the top first, but who stays there. Gain and maintain your position.

Today I am thankful for ...

_____

_____

_____

_____

_____

_____

In what areas did you gain and maintain today?

_____

_____

_____

_____

_____

_____

Turn your possibilities into promise.

Today I am thankful for ...

_____

_____

_____

_____

_____

_____

_____

How did you turn your possibilities into promise today?

_____

_____

_____

_____

_____

_____

_____

Amid adversity don't recede and retreat, instead recharge and reload.

Today I am thankful for ...

_____

_____

_____

_____

_____

_____

_____

How did you recharge and reload today?

_____

_____

_____

_____

_____

_____

_____

The only way to find out what your abilities are is to attempt to do what you think you can't. You may be surprised at the results.

Today I am thankful for ...

_____

_____

_____

_____

_____

What did you attempt to do today? How did you surprise yourself today?

_____

_____

_____

_____

_____

The fearful bird doesn't learn to fly until they take a leap of faith. Step out on faith and fly.

Today I am thankful for ...

_____

_____

_____

_____

_____

_____

_____

How did you step out on faith and fly today?

_____

_____

_____

_____

_____

_____

_____

_____

Some people are born with more and do less while others are born with less and do more. Which one are you?

Today I am thankful for ...

_____

_____

_____

_____

_____

_____

How did you do more with less today?

_____

_____

_____

_____

_____

_____

Allow your ambition to exceed the expectation. Don't stop where you're expected but surpass it.

Today I am thankful for ...

_____

_____

_____

_____

_____

_____

How did you surpass expectations today?

_____

_____

_____

_____

_____

_____

_____

The beauty of failure is learning where you went wrong. Life isn't all victories.

Today I am thankful for ...

_____

_____

_____

_____

_____

_____

_____

What did you learn today?

_____

_____

_____

_____

_____

_____

_____

To inspire others there must be something in you that's worthy of inspiration.

Today I am thankful for ...

_____

_____

_____

_____

_____

_____

_____

How were you an inspiration today?

_____

_____

_____

_____

_____

_____

_____

Your presence is a present.

Today I am thankful for ...

_____

_____

_____

_____

_____

_____

_____

How was your presence a present today?

_____

_____

_____

_____

_____

_____

_____

You're a winner but haven't won yet. Stay in the game.

Today I am thankful for ...

_____

_____

_____

_____

_____

_____

How did you win today?

_____

_____

_____

_____

_____

_____

_____

When encountering conflict remember when it all boils down it's nothing but hot air. Don't let your composure evaporate.

Today I am thankful for ...

_____

_____

_____

_____

_____

_____

How did you work to keep your composure today?

_____

_____

_____

_____

_____

_____

When it comes easily you don't value it; when it comes through diligence, you cherish it.

Today I am thankful for ...

_____

_____

_____

_____

_____

_____

How were you diligent today?

_____

_____

_____

_____

_____

_____

The cardinal principle of exercising, likewise in life, is to be capable of carrying your own weight.

Today I am thankful for ...

_____

_____

_____

_____

_____

_____

How did you carry your weight today?

_____

_____

_____

_____

_____

_____

_____

A key principle of robust growth is the ability to discern fertilizer from bullsh*t.

Today I am thankful for ...

_____

_____

_____

_____

_____

_____

_____

What did you discern today?

_____

_____

_____

_____

_____

_____

_____

The level of motivation impacts the depth of participation. Before you say, "I can't," you have already said "I <u>CAN</u>." Be great.

Today I am thankful for ...

_____

_____

_____

_____

_____

_____

To what did you say "I CAN" today?

_____

_____

_____

_____

_____

_____

The motive is the motivation.

Today I am thankful for ...

_____

_____

_____

_____

_____

_____

_____

What motivated you today?

_____

_____

_____

_____

_____

_____

_____

Even though you can't see the sun it doesn't mean it isn't shining somewhere.

Today I am thankful for ...

_____

_____

_____

_____

_____

_____

How did you shine today?

_____

_____

_____

_____

_____

_____

Second chances are for those who failed to take advantage of the first opportunity; however, they are not always guaranteed. Act first.

Today I am thankful for ...

_____

_____

_____

_____

_____

_____

_____

What did you act on today?

_____

_____

_____

_____

_____

_____

_____

They call Wednesday "hump day," but on Thursday there's another hill to climb.

Today I am thankful for ...

_____

_____

_____

_____

_____

_____

_____

What hills did you climb today?

_____

_____

_____

_____

_____

_____

_____

The courageous person does not let challenges become boundaries but uses them as motivation to propel themselves beyond limits.

Today I am thankful for ...

_____

_____

_____

_____

_____

_____

How did you propel beyond the limits today?

_____

_____

_____

_____

_____

_____

Make the moves you can make with the pieces you are given and maximize each move.

Today I am thankful for ...

_____

_____

_____

_____

_____

_____

_____

What moves did you make today?

_____

_____

_____

_____

_____

_____

_____

> # Creating more room in our lives allows more space for improvements and progression.

Today I am thankful for ...

_____

_____

_____

_____

_____

_____

_____

How did you create more room in your life today?

_____

_____

_____

_____

_____

_____

_____

Obtaining a sharper image begins with readjusting your eyes.

Today I am thankful for ...

_____
_____
_____
_____
_____
_____

How did you readjust your eyes today?

_____
_____
_____
_____
_____
_____

If you keep your head to the sky, you won't notice the darkness around. Face the sun and leave the shadow behind.

Today I am thankful for ...

_____

_____

_____

_____

_____

_____

How did you face the sun and leave the shadow behind today?

_____

_____

_____

_____

_____

_____

If you don't like the cards you're dealt, then change your hand. Deal yourself a winning hand by playing with the right deck.

Today I am thankful for ...

_____

_____

_____

_____

_____

_____

_____

How did you deal yourself a winning hand today?

_____

_____

_____

_____

_____

_____

_____

Opening Doors to Your Limitless Potential

> # There are many doors to be opened, but there are only a few keys. Find the key that unlocks your door.

Today I am thankful for ...

_____

_____

_____

_____

_____

_____

_____

What doors did you unlock today?

_____

_____

_____

_____

_____

_____

_____

71

Even when you feel HOPEless, there's still HOPE.

Today I am thankful for ...

_____

_____

_____

_____

_____

_____

What were you hopeful for today?

_____

_____

_____

_____

_____

_____

_____

To be the better person you must BE a better person.

Today I am thankful for ...

_____

_____

_____

_____

_____

_____

How were you the better person today?

_____

_____

_____

_____

_____

_____

Sometimes our experiences happen for a reason. Keep it moving so you can find the reason.

Today I am thankful for ...

_____

_____

_____

_____

_____

_____

_____

What reasons did you find today?

_____

_____

_____

_____

_____

_____

_____

Sometimes it's easier to embrace it than to resist it.

Today I am thankful for ...

_____

_____

_____

_____

_____

_____

_____

What did you embrace today?

_____

_____

_____

_____

_____

_____

Perseverance

Energy: you must know who charges your battery and who drains it.

Today I am thankful for ...

_____

_____

_____

_____

_____

_____

_____

Who charged your battery today?

_____

_____

_____

_____

_____

_____

_____

"Letting go" allows you to build and create an improved "you".

Today I am thankful for ...

_____

_____

_____

_____

_____

_____

How did you build and create an improved "you" today?

_____

_____

_____

_____

_____

_____

_____

A plant must shed the dead leaves to grow.

Today I am thankful for ...

_____

_____

_____

_____

_____

_____

_____

How did you shed the dead leaves and grow today?

_____

_____

_____

_____

_____

_____

_____

The seasoned hiker recognizes the mountains to climb and the ones to walk away from.

Today I am thankful for ...

_____

_____

_____

_____

_____

_____

_____

What mountains did you choose to climb or walk away from today?

_____

_____

_____

_____

_____

_____

_____

Bury the pain and grow from it.

Today I am thankful for ...

_____

_____

_____

_____

_____

_____

_____

What did you grow from today?

_____

_____

_____

_____

_____

_____

_____

Reduce stress now to avoid stress later.

Today I am thankful for ...

_____

_____

_____

_____

_____

_____

How did you reduce stress today?

_____

_____

_____

_____

_____

_____

_____

Sometimes the wrong turns are the right ones.

Today I am thankful for ...

_____

_____

_____

_____

_____

_____

What wrong turn ended up right today?

_____

_____

_____

_____

_____

_____

Don't spread your wings too far because extending too much for too many leaves you unable to soar.

Today I am thankful for ...

_____

_____

_____

_____

_____

_____

How did you soar today?

_____

_____

_____

_____

_____

_____

_____

Throughout your existence you'll realize life is a crash course with no manual and no test drive. Watch for the curves and don't speed.

Today I am thankful for ...

_____

_____

_____

_____

_____

_____

_____

How did you drive today?

_____

_____

_____

_____

_____

_____

_____

Sometimes in treacherous waters we must swim with the sharks to avoid being the bait.

Today I am thankful for ...

_____

_____

_____

_____

_____

_____

_____

How did you swim today?

_____

_____

_____

_____

_____

_____

_____

To reach the finish line, one must clear hurdles on the track of life.

Today I am thankful for ...

_____

_____

_____

_____

_____

_____

_____

What hurdles did you clear today?

_____

_____

_____

_____

_____

_____

_____

Life is similar to traffic. You can plan ahead, but you can't predict a roadblock or a detour.

Today I am thankful for ...

_____

_____

_____

_____

_____

_____

_____

How was life's traffic today?

_____

_____

_____

_____

_____

_____

_____

> ## If you cannot seize the day, then salvage what remains of it. The essence of recovery is discovery.

Today I am thankful for ...

_____

_____

_____

_____

_____

_____

How did you recover and discover today?

_____

_____

_____

_____

_____

_____

_____

To reach any milestone, you must first prepare to endure the long miles that lie ahead.

Today I am thankful for ...

_____

_____

_____

_____

_____

_____

_____

What long miles did you endure today?

_____

_____

_____

_____

_____

_____

_____

If you want to get to the other side, understand that it may be an uphill battle. Endure the climb.

Today I am thankful for ...

_____

_____

_____

_____

_____

_____

What uphill battles did you climb today?

_____

_____

_____

_____

_____

_____

_____

Either move away from the impediment that's hindering your upward mobility or move it out of your way and move forward. Regardless, keep it moving.

Today I am thankful for ...

_____

_____

_____

_____

_____

_____

How did you "keep it moving" today?

_____

_____

_____

_____

_____

> # The person that possesses the wherewithal to rise above circumstances and propel to new heights is not only dynamic but also aerodynamic.

Today I am thankful for ...

_____

_____

_____

_____

_____

_____

How were you aerodynamic today?

_____

_____

_____

_____

_____

_____

Catch the wind of destiny and sail to new heights by navigating through tumultuous waters. Set sail and be great.

Today I am thankful for ...

_____

_____

_____

_____

_____

_____

_____

How did you navigate through tumultuous waters today?

_____

_____

_____

_____

_____

_____

_____

In the palms of our hands, we secure the dexterity of our futures. Shape your future.

Today I am thankful for ...

_____

_____

_____

_____

_____

_____

_____

How did you shape your future today?

_____

_____

_____

_____

_____

_____

It's easy to run when the wind is at your back, but the true test arrives when your obstacle meets you face to face.

Today I am thankful for ...

_____

_____

_____

_____

_____

_____

_____

What obstacles did you meet face-to-face today?

_____

_____

_____

_____

_____

_____

_____

"I won't give up" translates to "I won't give in." Don't give up when it gets hard; make it hard to give in.

Today I am thankful for ...

_____

_____

_____

_____

_____

_____

_____

How did you refuse to give in today?

_____

_____

_____

_____

_____

_____

Those who push you to the top believe you belong there.

Today I am thankful for ...

_____

_____

_____

_____

_____

_____

_____

How were you pushed to be better today?

_____

_____

_____

_____

_____

_____

_____

_____

Ignore the crowd and hear the voice within because inside the stadium of life sometimes you can't determine who's cheering for you or against you.

Today I am thankful for ...

_____

_____

_____

_____

_____

_____

_____

How did you cheer for yourself today?

_____

_____

_____

_____

_____

_____

_____

> # Determination can't be stopped unless a person quits believing. There is no set time limit for accomplishments.

Today I am thankful for ...

_____

_____

_____

_____

_____

_____

How were you unstoppable today?

_____

_____

_____

_____

_____

_____

_____

Steps and stages, take it one step and one stage at a time.

Today I am thankful for ...

_____

_____

_____

_____

_____

_____

_____

_____

What steps did you take and what stages did you reach today?

_____

_____

_____

_____

_____

_____

_____

_____

Temporary pain transforms into long-term gain.

Today I am thankful for ...

_____

_____

_____

_____

_____

_____

How did you transform pains into gains today?

_____

_____

_____

_____

_____

_____

_____

Many things happen by chance and circumstance. Play the odds.

Today I am thankful for ...

_____
_____
_____
_____
_____
_____
_____

How did you play your odds today?

_____
_____
_____
_____
_____
_____
_____

One's conscience is guided from the guilt of mistakes and lessons learned. Mistakes are trials to help navigate your journey.

Today I am thankful for ...

_____

_____

_____

_____

_____

_____

_____

How did you navigate today?

_____

_____

_____

_____

_____

_____

_____

Conclusion

Quite often we major in the minor. To continue to grow and reach the best version of ourselves we must transform this mindset. Rather than focusing on the things we did not accomplish we must shift our perspective to be thankful for the things we have accomplished. I hope you continue to acknowledge the things you are thankful for and create a powerful new mindset and mentality.

Thank you for committing to yourself for the past 90 days by working daily and striving to be a better version of yourself. You deserve your greatness, and the world deserves your greatness. Peace, and blessings. Be great!

Biography

Mitch Mitchell, Ph.D. was born and raised in Washington, D.C., and holds a Ph.D. in Education with a focus on Leadership for Higher Education from Capella University. He holds an M.A. in Communications from Regent University, and a B.S. in Business Administration from Elizabeth City State University. He is a transformative servant-leader whose passion guided him to a career in higher education and birthed a drive to help others see their infinite potential. Dr. Mitchell, aka "The Dream Supporter", is a proponent for others to dream, believe and succeed. Dr. Mitchell, a "Hope Dealer", pours hope, passion, and positivity into others. He encourages them to write their own story to defy the odds and achieve their dreams. .

Remember, quite often we major in the minor. To continue to grow and achieve, we must transform this perspective. Rather than focusing on the things not accomplished, we will move forward with a shifted mindset to be thankful for the things we have accomplished.

Notes

_____

_____

_____

_____

_____

_____

_____

_____

_____

_____

_____

_____

_____

_____

_____

_____

_____

_____

_____

_____

_____

_____

_____

_____

_____

_____

_____

_____

_____

_____

_____

_____

_____

_____

_____

_____

_____

_____

_____

_____

_____

_____

_____

_____

Lightning Source UK Ltd.
Milton Keynes UK
UKHW020631040122
396581UK00006B/166